SONGS OF THE GILDED AGE

SELECTED AND EDITED BY MARGARET BRADFORD BONI
ARRANGED FOR VOICE, PIANO, AND GUITAR BY NORMAN LLOYD
ILLUSTRATED BY LUCILLE CORCOS
WITH AN INTRODUCTION BY WILLIAM SCHUMAN

GOLDEN PRESS · NEW YORK

Introduction

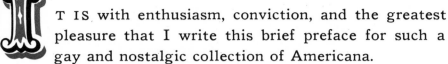

IT IS with enthusiasm, conviction, and the greatest pleasure that I write this brief preface for such a gay and nostalgic collection of Americana.

Our musical heritage is a rich and diverse one. It includes not only the ever-increasing wealth of our symphonic and operatic music, but the fabulous world of theater music, popular music, and folk music. Folk music usually bears the stamp of scholarly approval—after all, it was "discovered" and has the exotic appeal of never having been formally composed. Full-born it sprang spontaneously from the throats of the pioneers, the workers, the prisoners and slaves, the hillbillies, and the lads and lassies of the prairie. Although popular songs, on the other hand, have never enjoyed scholarly endorsement, they have been the living music for each succeeding generation and as such have formed an integral part of the American heritage.

This collection celebrates a wonderful period in American song with thoroughness and with the addition of entertaining and informative descriptive material about the songs. The musical arrangements are simple and within the means of the average pianist. But these arrangements are more than just simple: they are on a high professional plane and do the songs full justice.

A book such as this should go a long way toward reviving a time-honored American custom which seems of late to have faded—Sunday nights around the piano.

WILLIAM SCHUMAN
Composer and President of the Juilliard School of Music

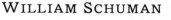

The editor wishes to express her appreciation to Mr. Herbert E. Marks for many courtesies, in particular his assistance in giving the definitive versions of these two songs, published by Edward B. Marks Music Corporation: "In the Good Old Summertime" and "There'll Be a Hot Time," for this edition.

Contents

Elsie from Chelsea

SONGS WITH girls' names, written in waltz form, were very popular for a time in the '90's. "Elsie from Chelsea" (this Chelsea is in London, not New York), with its catchy waltz rhythm and gay lyrics, is a happy example.

Words and Music by Harry Dacre

Tempo di Valse

1. Rid - ing one morn - ing, my fare I'd just paid, Oh, what a love - ly
2. Said she had no - where par - tic' - lar to go, Oh, what a love - ly
3. Went and we supped in a well - known ca - fé, Oh, what a love - ly

day! _____ Gave up my seat to a sweet lit - tle maid,
day! _____ Tak - ing the hint, I was not ver - y slow,
night! _____ I was bank - rupt be - fore we came a - way,

Oh, what a love - ly day! _____ Tho' she was real - ly a stran - ger to me,
Oh, what a gor - geous day! _____ Soon we were gush - ing as lov - ers can gush,
Oh, what a love - ly night! _____ P'r'aps you will guess that it end - ed in strife,

Streets of Cairo

(THE POOR LITTLE COUNTRY MAID)

AN AMUSING song of 1893 which mockingly imitates
the music used for the sensational dance of Little Egypt
at the Chicago World's Columbian Exposition.

Words and Music by James Thornton

1. I will sing you a song, And it won't be ver-y long, 'Bout a maid-en sweet, And she nev-er would do wrong. Ev-'ry-one said she was pret-ty, She was not long in the cit-y, All a-lone, oh, what a pit-y, Poor lit-tle maid.

2. She went out one night, Did this in-no-cent di-vine, With a nice young man Who in-vit-ed her to dine. Now he's sor-ry that he met her, And he nev-er will for-get her, In the fu-ture he'll know bet-ter, Poor lit-tle maid.

3. She was en-gaged As a pict-ure for to pose, To ap-pear each night In ab-bre-vi-at-ed clothes. All the dudes were in a flur-ry, For to catch her they did hur-ry, One who caught her now is sor-ry, Poor lit-tle maid.

1 & 2. She nev - er saw the streets of Cai - ro, On the Mid - way she had nev - er strayed.
3. She was much fair - er far than Tril - by, Lots of more men sor - ry will be,

f *simile*

She nev - er saw the kutch - y, kutch - y, Poor lit - tle coun - try maid.
If they don't try to keep a - way from this Poor lit - tle coun - try maid.

mf

MEET ME IN ST. LOUIS, LOUIS

IN NEW YORK, in a Broadway cafe, Sterling heard an order for a St. Louis beer called out to the bartender, whose name was Louis—"Another Louis, Louis!" The rhythm of the words intrigued him and gave him the idea for a timely song for the Louisiana Purchase Exposition in St. Louis in 1904. The song, sung by the millions who attended the fair, was adopted as the official song of the famous exposition. It had a great revival in 1944 when it was featured as the title song in the motion picture starring Judy Garland.

Words by Andrew B. Sterling

Music by Kerry Mills

Tempo di Valse

1. When Lou-is came home to the flat_____ He hung up his coat and his hat,_____ He gazed all a-round, but no wife-y he found, So he said "Where can Flos-sie be at?"_____ A note on the ta-ble he

2. The dress-es that hung in the flat hall_____ Were gone, she had tak-en them all._____ She took all his rings and the rest of his things;_____ The pic-ture he missed from the wall._____ "What! mov-ing?" the jan-i-tor

16

KENTUCKY BABE

A POPULAR glee club number of 1896.

Words by Richard Henry Buck

Music by Adam Geibel

Freely with sentiment

1. Skeet-ers am a hum-min' on de hon-ey-suck-le vine, Sleep, Ken-tuck-y Babe!
2. Dad-dy's in de cane-brake wid his lit-tle dog and gun, Sleep, Ken-tuck-y Babe!

Sand-man am a com-in' to dis lit-tle gal of mine,
Pos-som, fo' yo' break-fast when yo' sleep-in' time is done,

(Hum————)

Sleep, Ken-tuck-y Babe! Sil - v'ry moon am shin - in' in de
Sleep, Ken-tuck-y Babe! Bo - gie man - 'll ketch yo' sure un-

(Hum - - - - - - - - - -)

heab-ens up a - bove, Bob - o - link am pin - in' fo' his lit - tle la - dy love.
less yo' close yo' eyes, Wait - in' jes' out-side de doo' to take yo' by sur-prise.

(Hum - - - - - -) (Hum - - - - - - -) (Hum - - - - - - -)

You is might - y luck - y, Babe of old Ken-tuck - y, Close yo' eyes in sleep.____
Bes' be keep - in' shad - y, Pret - ty lit - tle la - dy, Close yo' eyes in sleep.____

20

CHORUS

Fly a - way, fly a - way Ken-tuck -y Babe, fly a - way to rest,

Fly a - way. Lay yo' tir - ed, lit -tle head on yo' mam-my's breast, Um _____

Um _____ close yo' eyes in sleep. _____

dim. al fine

21

HURRAH FOR BAFFIN'S BAY!

"HURRAH FOR BAFFIN'S BAY!" was one of the most successful songs in *The Wizard of Oz*, a musical show produced in 1903.

Words by Vincent P. Bryan

Music by Theodore F. Morse

Allegro moderato

1. 'Twas on the good ship Cus-pi-dor we sailed through Baf-fin's Bay; We
2. A brace of wild ducks perched up-on the star-board miz-zen clew; The

tied her to the O-cean while the Bul-warks ate some hay. The Cap-tain said "We'll tie the ship what-
Cap-tain spliced the brac-es and he braced us for a chew. He said "We'll dine on duck and wine, I

ev - er else be-tied;" And he drank a pint of gas-o-line with whis-key on the side. He had
know we'll have good luck, "But there was no Pip - er Heid-seick, so the Bo'-sun chased the duck. And he

lost his breath, but soon it was re - stored.___ It was mid-night in the gal - ley, it was
piped the chick-ens to the for - ward hatch.___ We were told to weigh the an - chor but the

one be-side the dock, But by the star-b'rd watch 'twas on - ly half past nine o'-clock. The
scales were full of ice. We could-n't weigh it all at once, we had to weigh it twice. The

first mate said, "Un-hitch the mules, we're go - ing thro' a lock." And then the Bo'-sun went and put the
sec - ond mate fell o - ver-board, it dried him to the skin. He got a-board with-out a rope, we

lar-board watch in "hock," For the good ship did-n't have a cent a-board.
could-n't rope him in, For he lit a-board us with a par-lor match.

CHORUS

A - vast! be - lay! hur - rah for Baf - fin's Bay! We could-n't find the pole be-cause the
A - vast! be - lay! hur - rah for Baf - fin's Bay! A whale be - gan to blub-ber, he was

bar - ber moved a - way. The boat was cold, we tho't we'd get the grip; So the
sore - ly tried one day. He mashed a sweet po - ta - to on a ship; But he

paint - ers put three coats up - on the ship. Hip, hip, hip, hip, hur - rah for Baf - fin's Bay!
found she was a Sar - a - to - ga chip. Hip, hip, hip, hip, hur - rah for Baf - fin's Bay!

24

The Bowery

THE BOWERY in the '90's was the center of the fast life of New York. Here the sharpers and the fakers carried on their trade among the sight-seers and naïve pleasure seekers. This account of a rustic's experiences there on his first visit to New York was sung in Charlie Hoyt's musical satire, *A Trip to Chinatown,* and became the hit song of the show. It was so popular that real estate values along the Bowery dropped, we are told, and there were vehement protests from the furious shopkeepers along the street.

Words by Charles H. Hoyt

Music by Percy Gaunt

Tempo di Valse

1. Oh! the night that I struck New York, I went
2. I had walk'd but a block or two, When up came a
3. Struck a place that they called a "dive," I was in

out for a qui - et walk. Folks who are "on to" the cit - y say,
fel - low and me he knew. Then a po - lice - man came walk - ing by,
luck to get out a - live. When the po - lice - man heard my woes,

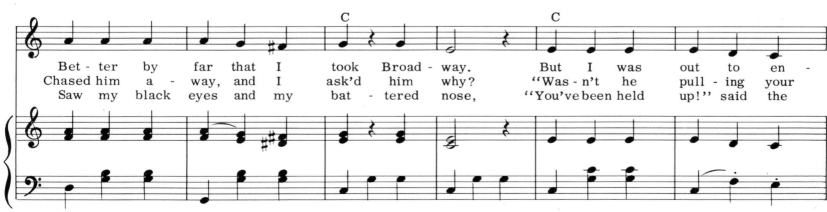

Bet - ter by far that I took Broad - way. But I was out to en -
Chased him a - way, and I ask'd him why? "Was - n't he pull - ing your
Saw my black eyes and my bat - tered nose, "You've been held up!" said the

CHORUS

The Bow - 'ry, the Bow - 'ry! They say such

things, and they do strange things on the Bow - 'ry! The

Bow - 'ry! I'll nev - er go there an - y more!_____

27

TOYLAND

THE CHARMING "Toyland" is from Victor Herbert's well-remembered and still popular operetta, *Babes in Toyland*, produced in New York in 1903.

Words by Glen Mac Donough

Music by Victor Herbert

Very slow and dreamily

1. When you've grown up my dears— And are as old as I,— You'll of-ten pon-der on the years That roll so swift-ly by, My dears, that roll so swift-ly by.— And of the man-y lands — You will have jour-neyed through,— You'll oft re-call The

2. When you've grown up my dears— There comes a drear-y day— When 'mid the locks of black ap-pears The first pale gleam of gray, My dears, the first pale gleam of gray.— Then of the past you'll dream— As gray-haired grown-ups do,— And seek once more its

poco animato e cresc.

On the Banks of the Wabash, Far Away

PAUL DRESSER was born in Terre Haute, Indiana, on the banks of the Wabash River. He ran away from home as a boy, worked with several minstrel troupes in various humble capacities, and eventually became one of the foremost writers of popular songs of his day, and one of the most loved figures in Tin Pan Alley. Generous to a fault, always genial, with an endless store of good stories and jokes, he was a most welcome figure in all the bars of New York City.

Theodore Dreiser, his brother, writes that his songs, full of sentimentalities, "set forth with amazing accuracy the moods, the reactions, and the aspirations of the exceedingly humble, intellectually and emotionally." His most famous song, "On the Banks of the Wabash, Far Away," has a folk-like quality which places it among the best folk music of the United States. It has been chosen as the official song of the state of Indiana.

Words and Music by Paul Dresser

1. Round my In-di-an-a home-stead wave the corn-fields, In the dis-tance loom the wood-lands clear and cool. Of - ten
2. Man-y years have passed since I strolled by the riv-er, Arm in arm with sweet-heart Mar - y by my side. It was

30

GIVE MY REGARDS TO BROADWAY

LITTLE JOHNNY JONES, Cohan's big stage hit of 1905, contained the well-known "Give My Regards to Broadway" and "The Yankee Doodle Boy." The show opened at the Liberty Theatre in New York on November 7, 1904. Cohan wrote the book, the lyrics, and the music for the show and was the star singer, actor, dancer, and stage manager as well. The show closed after only two months, but Cohan took it on the road, brought it back to New York in 1905, and established it as a definite hit. From this time on Cohan dominated the musical theatre on Broadway, to such an extent, in fact, that his biographer, Ward Montgomery, wrote of him, "After the turn of the century, Cohan *was* Broadway."

Words and Music by George M. Cohan

Tempo di Marcia

1. Did you ev - er see two Yan-kees part up - on a
2. Say hel - lo to dear old Co - ney Isle, if on there you

for - eign shore;_____ When the good ship's just a - bout to
chance to be;_____ When you're at the Wal - dorf, have a

start for old New York once more? _____ With __ tear-dimmed eye they
smile and charge it up to me. _____ Men-tion my name ev -'ry

say good -- bye, they're friends, with - out a doubt; _____ When the man on the
place you go, as 'round the town you roam. _____ Wish you'd call on my

pier shouts, "Let them clear," as the ship strikes out. _____
gal, now re - mem - ber old pal, when you get back home. _____

CHORUS

Give my re - gards to Broad - way, re - mem-ber me to Her - ald

34

THERE'LL BE A HOT TIME

THE TUNE of this popular song of the Spanish-American War was originally a band tune written years earlier for the famous McIntyre and Heath minstrels by their bandmaster, Theodore Metz. The words were added later by Joe Hayden, a singer in the minstrel troupe. One of many stories attributes his inspiration to the posters announcing the coming of the McIntyre and Heath minstrels to Old Town, Louisiana, and promising everybody who turned out a "Hot Time in Old Town" that night. Hayden, seeing the posters, was inspired by the slogan to write words for Metz's band tune, and the minstrels opened their program that night in Old Town with the song.

Words by Joe Hayden

Music by Theodore A. Metz

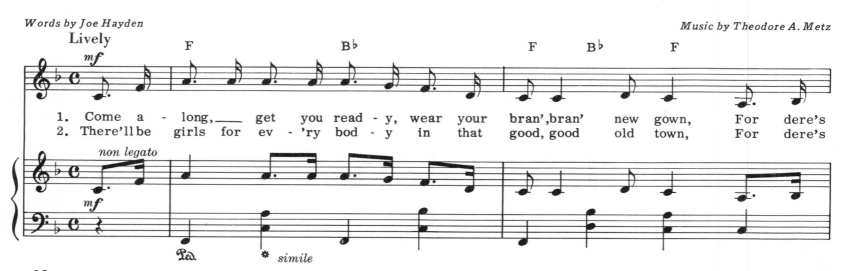

1. Come a - long,___ get you read - y, wear your bran',bran' new gown, For dere's
2. There'll be girls for ev - 'ry bod - y in that good, good old town, For dere's

gwine to be a meet-ing in that good, good___ old town, Where you
Miss Con-so-la Da-vis an' dere's Miss Gon-do-lia Brown, And dere's

know-ded ev-'ry-bod-y and dey all know-ded you, And you've
Miss Jo-han-na Beas-ly, she am dressed all in red, I just

got a rab-bit's foot to keep a-way de hoo-doo.
hugged her and I kissed her and to me then she said:

When you hear that the preach-ing does be-gin, Bend down low for to
"Please, oh, please, oh, ___ do not let me fall. You're all mine and I

without pedal

drive a-way your sin. And when you gets re - li - gion you ___
love you best of all; And you must be my man ___ or I'll

want to shout and sing, There'll be a hot time in the old town to-night, my ba - by.
have no man at all. There'll be a hot time in the old town to-night, my ba - by."

CHORUS

When you hear dem-a bells go ding, ling, ling, All join 'round and sweet-ly you must sing; And when the

verse am through, in the cho-rus all join in, There'll be a hot time in the old town to - night. ___

38

MY SWEETHEART'S THE MAN IN THE MOON

THORNTON, genial, undependable, bibulous, was one of the greatest of the Tin Pan Alley song writers and comedians. He began his career as a singing waiter at an East Side cafe in New York. Bonnie Thornton, his wife, a well-known singer of the day, worked there also, and part of her job, it is told, was to keep her husband from spending all of his money on drink.

Thornton, returning home from a drinking spree on Independence Day, was met with Bonnie's tearful reproof and her sadly expressed doubt of his love and fidelity. Quickly he reassured her with the words, "My sweetheart's the man in the moon." The words gave him the title and idea for one of his greatest songs, which was later sung with enormous success by Bonnie at Tony Pastor's 14th Street Theatre.

Words and Music by James Thornton

1. Ev-'ry-bod-y has a sweet-heart un-der-neath the rose,
2. I have of-ten won-der'd where he spends his time all day,

"Ev-'ry-bod-y loves a bod-y," so the old song goes.
P'rhaps he has an-oth-er sweet-heart man-y miles a-way.

I've a sweet-heart, you all know him just as well as me.
May-be some sweet, dark-hair'd maid-en, dai-ly he does woo.

Ev -'ry ev'-ning I can see him, short-ly aft - er tea.
But as long as I don't catch him, I'll be - lieve him true.

CHORUS

Tempo di Valse

1. My sweet-heart's the man in the moon, _____ I'm go-ing to
2. Last night while the stars bright - ly shone, _____ He told me through

mar - ry him soon. _____ 'Twould fill me with bliss, just to
Love's Tel - e - phone _____ That when we were wed, he'd go

give him one kiss, But I know that a doz - en I nev - er would
ear - ly to bed, And nev - er stay out with the boys, so he

41

miss. I'll go up in a great big bal - loon, _____ And
said. We are go - ing to mar - ry next June, _____ The

see my sweet - heart in the moon. _____ Then be - hind some dark cloud Where no
wed - ding takes place in the moon. _____ A sweet lit - tle Ve - nus we'll fon -

one is al - low'd, I'll make love to the man in the moon. _____
dle be - tween us, When I wed my old man in the moon. _____

42

I Love You Truly

CARRIE JACOBS was born in Janesville, Wisconsin. Her father, who had lost all his money in a grain panic, died when she was twelve, and the rest of her childhood was spent with her grandfather. At the age of twenty-five, she married Dr. Frank L. Bond, her hometown physician. Later they moved to Chicago, and there her husband died in an accident, leaving her practically penniless and with a small son to support.

Earlier she had had some success in writing children's songs, and she now turned again to song writing. Her first book, *Seven Songs as Unpretentious as the Wild Rose*, contained "I Love You Truly" and "Just A-Wearyin' for You," both of which became among the most popular of American songs.

Later, in New York, her simple, sentimental songs were not popular. She returned to Chicago and years of struggle, illness and poverty began. As it had before, help came from a friend and eventually she achieved permanent success. She died in Hollywood at the age of eighty-four, honored and wealthy.

Words and Music by Carrie Jacobs-Bond

1. I love you tru - ly, ____ tru - ly, dear. Life with its sor - row, ____ life with its tear, Fades in - to dreams when I feel you are near, For I love you tru - ly, tru - ly, dear.

2. Ah! love, 'tis some - thing to feel your kind hand. Ah! yes, 'tis some - thing by your side to stand. Gone is the sor - row, ____ Gone doubt and fear, For you love me tru - ly, tru - ly, dear.

I Love You in the Same Old Way

(DARLING SUE)

EARLY in the eighteen-nineties, from the song-writing partnership of Ford and Bratton, came one of the most famous songs about the neglected child, "Only Me." In 1896, the same song-writing pair produced another big success, but of quite a different type, "I Love You in the Same Old Way."

Words by Walter H. Ford

Music by John W. Bratton

1. Bright was the day, bells ring-ing gay, When to church I brought my Sue.
2. Un-der a tree, plant-ed by we, Where she lies there's room for me.

I felt so proud, 'fore all the crowd, Just to think that I'd won her.
In shine or storm, o-ver her form, I lay bunch-es of po-sies,

Dressed up in her ging-ham gown,___ Just to come with me to town,___
Flow-ers that she loved so well.___ Not the kind that town folks sell,___

BLUE BELL

MORSE, a native of Washington, D.C., ran away from the Maryland Military Academy at the age of fourteen and went to New York. At fifteen his first composition was published, and by the time he was twenty-four he had become successful enough to have his own publishing business. "Blue Bell" was the great Madden-Morse hit of the year 1904.

Words by Edward Madden

Music by Theodore F. Morse

Tempo di marcia

1. Blue Bell, the dawn is wak - ing, Sweet-heart, you must not sigh.
2. Blue Bell, they are re - turn - ing, Each greets a sweet-heart true.

Blue Bell, my heart is break - ing, I've come to say good - bye.
Blue Bell, your heart is yearn - ing, Nev - er a one greets you.

Hear how the bu - gle's call - ing, Call - ing to each brave heart.
Sad - ly they tell the sto - ry, Tell how he fought and fell;

48

MIGHTY LAK' A ROSE

THIS MOST pleasing and popular song was
written by Nevin in 1901, the year of his death.

Words by Frank L. Stanton

Music by Ethelbert Nevin

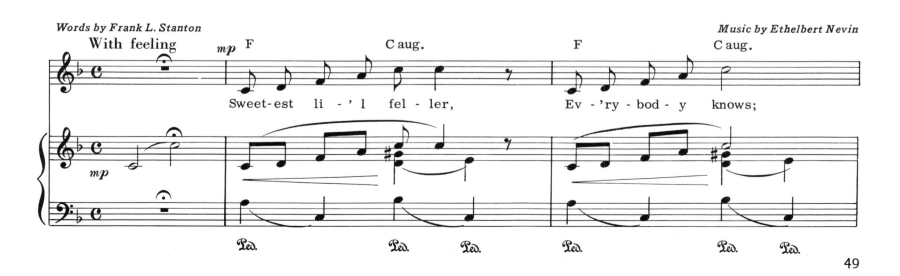

Sweet-est li-'l fel-ler, Ev-'ry-bod-y knows;

kiss 'im in his sleep.___ Sweet-est li - l fel - ler, Ev -'ry-bod - y knows;

Dun - no what to call 'im, But he might - y lak' a rose! Look-in' at his Mam - my Wid

eyes so shin - y blue, Mek' you think that heav'n___ Is com - in' clost ter you!

WITH ALL HER FAULTS I LOVE HER STILL

A MOST sentimental ballad of the year 1888, and one of Rosenfeld's greatest hits. The faults of the lady are not enumerated in the song, but the title implying these faults has become a folk saying.

Words and Music by Monroe H. Rosenfeld

1. With all her faults I love her still, And e-ven though the world should scorn; No love like hers, my heart can thrill, Al-though she's made that heart for-lorn! Tho' oth-er hearts have won her love, I bear for her no dreams of

2. She went a-way one sum-mer day, And nev-er came a-gain to me. And since that day I long and pray That I may pass Life's drear-y sea! I see her now as first we met, The sun-light shin-ing o'er her

3. With all her faults I love her still, Al-though her love for me is dead. In ev-'ry dream Her smile doth beam, Nor care I what the world hath said! I know that she'll re-turn a-gain, Al-though her face no more I

Gypsy Love Song

VICTOR HERBERT, a most prolific and facile composer, made perhaps his largest contribution to American music in his compositions for the popular theatre. In less than forty years, in addition to numerous other works, he wrote forty operettas, the first being *Princess Ananias* in 1894. In 1898, he wrote *The Fortune Teller,* an operetta with a Hungarian setting into which was interpolated the popular "Gypsy Love Song."

Words by Harry B. Smith

Music by Victor Herbert

Molto tranquillo

The birds of the for-est are call-ing for thee, ____ And the shades and the glades ____ are lone-ly. ____ Sum-mer is there with her blos-soms

ALEXANDER

THE DRAWLING pronunciation of the name "Alexander" in a vaudeville act of McIntyre and Heath seems to have inspired this amusing ragtime song of 1904. Von Tilzer's syncopated musical imitation of the pronunciation resulted in a highly successful song, still popular and still good ragtime.

Words by Andrew B. Sterling

Music by Harry Von Tilzer

Moderato

1. Look here, Alexander, I was only fooling When I said another man my heart was ruling. All the day I think of no one else but you.

2. Look here, Alexander, say that you remember. You ain't done a stroke of work since last December. Who went out a-washin', worked all day for you?

G   D7   G   A7

Hon - est, Al - ex - an - der, Won't you please be - lieve_ me?   It would break my heart in two if
Lis - ten, Al - ex - an - der, you were keep - in' cas - es.   While I took in scrub - bin', you just

D7   G   G7   E7   A min.   A7   D7

you should leave_ me. Won't you take_ me back, babe,   and I'll al - ways be
played the ra - ces. Say, if that_ ain't love, babe,   no gal ev - er loved

G   D   A7

true;_   Nev - er let an - oth - er man make   eyes   at me._
true._   I don't want to talk a - bout the   things   I've done,_

59

I'll be just as sweet as an-y gal can be,___ You can be the "Boss," I'll let you
I just want to say that you're ma on-ly one.___ I'll put up a wash-in' sign out-

have your way,___ Al-ex-an-der, won't you let me stay?___
side the door,___ Al-ex-an-der, take me back once more.___

CHORUS

Can't you see the rain and hail am fast-ly fall-ing, Al-ex-an-der?___

Don't you hear your la-dy love a soft-ly call-ing, Al-ex-

an - der? _____

G   **B7**

Take me to your heart a - gain and

E7   **A min.**   **E7 A min.**

call me hon - ey; All I want is lov - in', I don't want your mon - ey. Al - ex -

G   **A7**   **D7**

an - der, tell ___ me, don't you love your ba - - by no

G   **C+6**   **G**

more? _____

The Rosary

NEVIN, born in Edgeworth, Pennsylvania, died in New Haven, Connecticut, at the age of thirty-eight. He wrote many songs of pleasing sentimentality. "The Rosary," written in 1898, sold six million copies in its first thirty years. It still has tremendous vogue.

Words by Robert Cameron Rogers

Music by Ethelbert Nevin

Lento ed intimo

The hours I spent with thee, dear heart, Are as a string of pearls to me. I count them o - ver, ev - 'ry one a - part, My ro - sa - ry, my

ro-sa-ry! Each hour a pearl, each pearl a pray'r To still a heart in ab-sence wrung.

I tell each bead un-to the end, And there a cross is hung! O mem-o-ries that bless and

burn! O bar-ren gain and bit-ter loss! I kiss each bead, and strive at

last to learn To kiss the cross, sweet-heart! To kiss the cross.

63

The Band Played On

PALMER, a young actor and occasional writer of songs, paused one morning to listen to a German band playing on the street outside his house. Summoned to breakfast by his sister Pauline, he answered, "One moment; let the band play on." To both of them the words immediately suggested a title for a song, and forthwith Palmer wrote the music and lyrics for the story of Casey and the Strawberry Blonde. Unable to sell the song, he put it aside.

Years later Charles Ward heard it, recognized its possibilities, and bought it from Palmer. He made a few changes, published it with his name as composer, and within a few years, thanks to his tireless efforts, the song became successful. It sold more than a million copies.

Words by John F. Palmer

Music by Charles B. Ward

1. Matt Casey formed a social club that beat the town for style, And hir-ed for a meet-ing place a hall._____ When pay day came a-round each week they greased the floor with wax, And_ danced with noise and vig-or at the ball._____ Each

2. Such kiss-ing in the cor-ner and such whisp'-ring in the hall, And tell-ing tales of love be-hind the stairs._____ As Ca-sey was the fa-vor-ite and he that ran the ball, Of_ kiss-ing and love-mak-ing did his share._____ At

3. Now when the dance was o-ver and the band played "Home, Sweet Home," They played a tune at Ca-sey's own re-quest._____ He thank'd them ver-y kind-ly for the fa-vors they had shown, Then he'd waltz once with the girl that he loved best._____ Most

played on._____ He'd glide cross the floor with the girl he a-

dor'd, and the band played on._____ But his brain was so load-ed it

near-ly ex-plod-ed; The poor girl would shake with a-larm._____ He'd ne'er leave the

girl with the straw-ber-ry curls, And the band played on._____

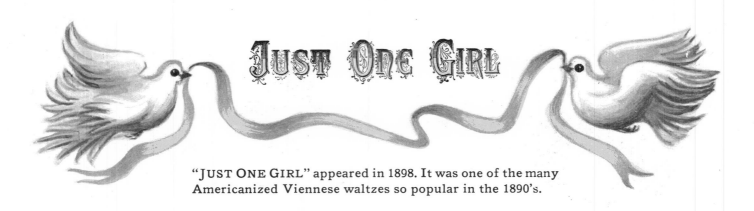

JUST ONE GIRL

"JUST ONE GIRL" appeared in 1898. It was one of the many Americanized Viennese waltzes so popular in the 1890's.

Words by Karl Kennett

Music by Lyn Udall

1. I'm in love with a sweet lit - tle girl - ie, on - ly one, on - ly one. I meet her each morn - ing quite ear - ly, rain or sun, rain or sun. To work we go walk - ing to - geth - er,

2. To be mar - ried we're old e - nough, plen - ty, she and I, she and I. She's eight - een and I will be twen - ty, by - and - by, by - and - by. Al - though we are short as to mon - ey,

68

And Her Golden Hair Was Hanging Down Her Back

A CYNICAL story of a maid, simple and naïve, who left her village for a visit to the big city of New York and returned home quite changed—no longer shy, "But alas and alack! With a naughty little twinkle in her eye."

Words and Music by Felix McGlennon and Monroe H. Rosenfeld

1. There was once a sim-ple maid-en came to New York on a trip, And her gold-en hair was hang-ing down her back. Her cheeks were like the ros-es, she'd a pout up-on her lip, And her gold-en hair was hang-ing down her back. When she
2. She tod-dled down Broad-way, a bash-ful smile up-on her face, And her gold-en hair was hang-ing down her back. A bit of nice blue rib-bon kept her ring-lets in their place, For her gold-en hair was hang-ing down her back. Of
3. She took his arm in con-fi-dence, she liked his pleas-ant ways, And her gold-en hair was hang-ing down her back. At all the dam-sels pass-ing by she stared in great a-maze, And her gold-en hair was hang-ing down her back. She
4. They drank un-til the art-less man so ver-y wea-ry grew, And her gold-en hair was hang-ing down her back. She took his chain and tick-er, and his dia-mond breast pin, too, And her gold-en hair was hang-ing down her back. Then
5. Now, gen-tle-folks, I warn you all to shun the sim-ple maid, When her gold-en hair is hang-ing down her back. If any such you run a-cross just don't you be a-fraid, When her gold-en hair is hang-ing down her back. Just

land - ed at the sta - tion here she took a lit - tle stroll;
course, she knew her man - ners; she'd been taught to be po - lite,
told him she was thirst - y, "Oh, all right," said he, "good biz,"
si - lent - ly she left him as he slum - bered in a chair,
skip the gut - ter, cross the street, or take an - oth - er lane,

At
So
He
In -
Or

BEDELIA

A GOOD TUNE and a nice use of Irish folk material resulted in one of the outstanding successes of the song-writing
partnership of Jerome and Schwartz. It appeared in 1903.

Words by William Jerome

Music by Jean Schwartz

1. There's a charm-ing I-rish la-dy with a ro-guish win-ning way, Who has kept my heart a-bump-in' and a-jump-in' night and day. She's a flow-er from Kil-lar-ney with a Tip-pe-rar-y smile, She's the best that ev-er

2. If you love me,— Be-de-lia, half as much as I love you, There is noth-ing in this world can ev-er cut our love in two. For I'll give you all my mon-ey on the day that we are wed, I will cook for you and

74

Say some - thing sweet Be - de - lia, _____

Your voice ____ I like to hear. _____ Oh, Be - de - lia, e - lia, e - li a, I've made

up my mind to steal ya, steal ya, steal ya, _____ Be - de - lia dear. _____

76

Two Little Girls In Blue

FOR A period in the '90's, mawkishly sentimental songs about children were very popular. Song writers wrote of neglected children, of lost children, of good children, of children used as an audience to whom some member of another generation related his own life's tragedy. "Two Little Girls" is of this last type—a melodramatic misunderstanding told to a little boy by his uncle.

Words and Music by Charles Graham

1. An old man gazed on a pho - to - graph in the lock - et he'd worn for years._____ His neph - ew then asked him the rea - son why that pic - ture had caused him tears._____ "Come, lis - ten," he said, "I will

2. "That pic - ture is one of those girls," he said, "and to me she was once a wife._____ I thought her un - faith - ful, we quar - reled, lad, and part - ed that night for life._____ My fan - cy of jeal - ous - y

tell you, lad, a sto - ry that's strange but true._____ Your fa - ther and
wronged a heart, a heart that was good and true;_____ For two bet - ter

I, at the school one day, met two lit - tle girls in blue."_____
girls nev - er lived than they, those two lit - tle girls in blue."_____

CHORUS

"Two lit - tle girls in blue, lad, two lit - tle girls in

blue,_____ They were sis - ters, we were broth - ers, and

78

The Maiden with the Dreamy Eyes

A SONG of 1901 from the famous song-writing partnership of Cole and John-son. It was sung most successfully by Anna Held (at that time married to Florenz Ziegfeld) in the musical show *The Little Duchess*.

Words by J. W. Johnson

Music by Bob Cole

1. No doubt you've seen the maid-en with the dim-ple in her chin, A ver-y charm-ing girl is she. The maid with feet and an-kles that a beau-ty prize would win, A ver-y pret-ty sight to see. But the

2. The maid-en with the dream-y eyes you can-not well re-sist, There's mag-net-is-m in those eyes. They make a fel-low feel that she is long-ing to be kissed, And there is where the dan-ger lies. Al-though

3. You get a-board a Broad-way car and get a seat per-haps, That's quite a luck-y thing to do. While a-ged fe-male pas-sen-gers are hang-ing on the straps, And ev-'ry-bod-y stares at you. With the

maid - en that's most charm - ing, All your war - i - ness dis - arm - ing, With se -
mar - riage you're op - pos - ing, When you see her eyes half clos - ing, With you can -
crowd that still comes pil - ing, Comes a maid with eyes be - guil - ing, And you

duc - tive - ness a - larm - ing, Is the maid - en with the dream - y eyes.
not re - sist pro - pos - ing To the maid - en with the dream - y eyes.
give your seat up smil - ing To the maid - en with the dream - y eyes.

CHORUS

There are eyes of blue, There are brown eyes too; There are eyes of ev - 'ry

size and eyes of ev - 'ry hue. But__ I sur - mise, That if

you are wise, You'll be care - ful of the maid - en with the dream - y eyes.

82

Little Annie Rooney

NOLAN'S song first appeared in England and was sung by him in English music halls in the late '80's. It drifted to America, was introduced here by Annie Hart at the Old London Theatre and immediately became one of the big hit songs of the year. Nolan, however, realized nothing from its success, for the song appeared before the enactment of the international copyright law, was pirated by American publishers, and the earnings from its fabulous sheet-music sales were theirs. Embittered and heartbroken by this experience, Nolan stopped composing altogether.

Words and Music by Michael Nolan

Tempo di Valse

1. A win - ning way, a pleas - ant smile; Dress'd so neat but quite in style; Mer - ry words your time to while, Has lit - tle An - nie Roon - ey. Ev - 'ry eve - ning, rain or shine, I
2. The par - lor's small, but neat and clean, And set with taste so sel - dom seen; And you can bet the house - hold queen Is lit - tle An - nie Roon - ey. The fire burns cheer - ful - ly and bright, As a
3. We've been en - gaged close on a year, The hap - py time is draw - ing near. I'll wed the one I love so dear, My lit - tle An - nie Roon - ey. My friends de - clare I am in jest, They

"SWEET ADELINE" was composed in 1896 by Armstrong, then eighteen and working in a jewelry store in Boston; the words were written later by Gerard, a postal clerk in New York. It was originally called "Down Home in Old New England," and the line "You're the flower of my heart" ended with the name "Sweet Rosalie," which proved quite unsingable. A poster announcing Adelina Patti's farewell tour suggested the change of the name to Adeline. The song, thus changed, was then introduced by the Quaker City Four at Hammerstein's Victoria Theatre with tremendous success. It is still a favorite song of all harmonizers.

You're the Flower of My Heart, Sweet Adeline

Words by Richard H. Gerard (Husch)

Music by Harry Armstrong

1. In the eve - ning when I sit a - lone a -
2. I can see your smil - ing face as when we

dream - ing___ Of days gone by, love,___ to me so dear,
wan - dered___ Down by the brook - side,___ just you and I.

There's a
And it

Sweet Rosie O'Grady

"A BIT of musical lavender that blossoms perennially from its Bowery roots is 'Sweet Rosie O'Grady'," says Douglas Gilbert. The writing of this simple, sentimental ballad is credited to Maude Nugent. Certainly it was she who sang it to success at Tony Pastor's in 1896.

Words and Music by Maude Nugent

1. Just down a-round the cor-ner of the street where I re-side, There
2. I nev-er shall for-get the day she prom-ised to be mine; As

lives the cut-est lit-tle girl that I have ev-er spied. Her
we sat tell-ing love tales in the gold-en sum-mer-time. 'Twas

name is Rose O' Gra-dy and I don't mind tell-ing you, That
on her fin-ger that I placed a small en-gage-ment ring, While

she's the sweet-est lit - tle Rose the gar - den ev - er grew.
in the trees, the lit - tle birds this song they seemed to sing!

CHORUS Valse

Sweet Ro - sie O' Gra - dy, My dear lit - tle

Rose._____ She's my stead - y la - dy,

Most ev - 'ry-one knows._____ And when we are mar -

90

She Is More To Be Pitied, Than Censured

A HEARTRENDING ballad of the righteously maudlin type.

Words and Music by William B. Gray

1. At the old con-cert hall on the Bow-'ry,_____ 'Round a ta-ble were seat-ed one night _____ A _____ crowd of young fel-lows ca-rous-ing,_____ With__ them life seemed cheer-ful and bright._____ At the ver-y next
2. There's an old-fash-ioned church round the cor-ner_____ Where the neigh-bors all gath-ered one day_____ While the par-son was preach-ing a ser-mon_____ O'er a soul that had just passed a-way._____ 'Twas this same way-ward

ta - ble was seat - ed _____ A ____ girl who had fal - len to
girl from the Bow - 'ry, _____ Who a life of ad - ven - ture had

shame._____ All the young fel-lows jeered at her weak-ness_____
led._____ Did the cler-gy-man jeer at her down-fall?_____

Till they heard an old wom-an ex - claim:_____
No, he asked for God's mer - cy and said:_____

CHORUS

She is more to be pit-ied than cen-sured,_____ She is more to be

helped than de - spised._____ She is on-ly a las-sie who ven-tured_____

On life's storm-y path, ill ad - vised. Do not scorn her with words fierce and
bit - ter; Do not laugh at her shame and down - fall. For a mo-ment just
stop and con - sid - er That a man was the cause of it all.

A Bird In A Gilded Cage

AN AMUSING story is told about this song, which Von Tilzer spoke of as "The key that opened for me the door to wealth and fame." Lamb came to him with the lyrics and asked him to write the music for them. Von Tilzer, greatly intrigued by the title, agreed to do so on one condition: that Lamb make it quite clear in his lyrics that the girl in the song was married to the wealthy old man, not living with him in sin. This being agreed to, he wrote the music for the song one afternoon and, in the evening, dropped in at a tawdry saloon, anxious to try it out. He sat at the piano and played and sang it through. When he finished, he noticed that some of the girls present were weeping. "If these ladies weep real tears over my song," he said, "I believe I have composed a hit."

Words by Arthur J. Lamb   *Music by Harry Von Tilzer*

1. The ball-room was filled with fash-ion's throng, It shone with a thou-sand lights; And there was a wom-an who passed a-
2. I stood in a church-yard just at eve, When sun-set a-dorned the West; And looked at the peo-ple who'd come to

On A Sunday Afternoon

VON TILZER claims that this gay, lilting waltz tune came to him as he was lazing in the sunshine on a beach one Sunday afternoon. It seems that he awoke suddenly with the line "They work hard on Monday, but one day that's fun day," and the realization that he had the makings of a hit song. With the help of Sterling the song was quickly written, and within a few days was being sung all over New York. The sales went over the million mark.

Words by Andrew B. Sterling

Music by Harry Von Tilzer

goes with his Pearl-ie, his own lit-tle girl-ie, to some nice place. ____
Sun-day at two, I'll be wait-ing for you on the old Iron Pier."

When You Were Sweet Sixteen

ANOTHER DRINKING spree and Thornton's subsequent assurance to Bonnie that he loved her as he had when she was sweet sixteen were the inspiration for the song which was his last big success. It was published in 1898 and is still immensely popular, especially with barbershop quartets.

Words and Music by James Thornton

1. When first I saw the love-light in your eye, _____ And
2. Last night I dreamt I held your hand in mine, _____ And

heard thy voice, like sweet-est mel-o-dy, _____ Speak words of love to my en-rap-tur'd
once a-gain you were my hap-py bride. _____ I kiss'd you as I did in auld lang

soul, _____ The world had naught but joy in store for me. _____ E'en
syne, _____ As to the church we wan-der'd side by side. _____ The

first I met you on the vil-lage green; _____ Come to me, or my dream of love is o'er, _____ I love you as I lov'd you When you were sweet, when you were sweet six-teen.

A Stein Song

THIS IS not the "Maine Stein Song," which was sung to popularity by Rudy Vallee, but a fine old convivial ditty of 1896, which is still considered by Sigmund Spaeth one of the best for "harmonious rafter raising."

Words by Richard Hovey   *Music by Frederic Field Bullard*

With gusto

1. Give a rouse, then, in the May-time, For a life that knows no
2. Oh, ___ we're all frank and twen-ty When the spring is in the

fear! Turn ___ night-time in-to day-time With the sun-light of good
air; And we've faith and hope a-plen-ty, And we've life and love to

Just A-wearyin' for You

FROM *Seven Songs as Unpretentious as the Wild Rose*. See page 43 for note.

Words by Frank L. Stanton

Music by Carrie Jacobs-Bond

1. Just a-wear-y-in' for you, All the time a-feel-in' blue,
2. Morn-in' comes, the birds a-wake, Used to sing so for your sake.
3. Eve-nin' comes, I miss you more When the dark gloom's round the door.

Wish-in' for you, wond'-rin' when You'll be com-in' home a-gain. Rest-less, don't know
But there's sad-ness in the notes That come trill-in' from their throats. Seem to feel your
Seems just like you or-ter be There to o-pen it for me. Latch goes tink-lin',

what to do, Just a-wear-y-in' for you.
ab-sence, too, Just a-wear-y-in' for you.
thrills me through, Sets me wear-y-in' for you.

Down Where The Wurzburger Flows

VON TILZER, who for a time had been a partner in the Shapiro and Bernstein Publishing Co., started his own publishing house in 1902. Within the first four years he had brought out seven major hits. Among these were four of his most famous songs, one of them "Down Where the Wurzburger Flows." This was a drinking song, written to order for a musical show, *The Wild Rose*. It never got into the show, however; the show's librettist, Harry B. Smith, thought he could write a better one.

Words by Vincent P. Bryan

Music by Harry Von Tilzer

Tempo di Valse — freely

A7   D min.   A dim. 7   C   E dim. 7   G7   F   F#7   G7

he - mia my lone - ly heart pines, And I long to be there once a - gain.____
an - o, a cold stein of beer, And a fel - low who knows how to play.____

CHORUS

E min.   G7   C   E7   A min.   C maj. 7   F   A7

Take me down, down, down where the Wurz - burg - er flows, flows,

111

Just Tell Them That You Saw Me

THIS EARLY and popular Dresser song, according to Theodore Dreiser, supposedly followed an actual encounter with a girl whose life had "gone to wreck on the shores of love."

Words and Music by Paul Dresser

1. While stroll-ing down the street one eve up - on mere plea-sure bent, 'Twas af-ter busi-ness wor-ries of the day,___ I saw a girl who shrank from me in whom I re-cog-nized My school-mate in a vil-lage far a - way.___ "Is

2. "Your cheeks are pale, your face is thin, come tell me, were you ill? When last we met your eye shone clear and bright.___ Come home with me when I go, Madge, the change will do you good, Your Moth-er won-ders where you are to - night." "I

With pedal throughout

that you, Madge,"I said to her, she quick-ly turned a - way. "Don't
long to see them all a - gain, but not just yet," she said; "'Tis

turn a - way, Madge, I am still your friend;_____ Next week I'm go - ing back to see the
pride a - lone that's keep-ing me a - way. _____ Just tell them not to wor - ry, for I'm

old folks and I thought Per - haps some mes-sage you would like to send."_____
all right, don't you know? Tell Moth - er I am com - ing home some day."_____

CHORUS
"Just tell them that you saw me," She said, "They'll know the rest. Just

In the Good Old Summertime

ONE OF the most joyous songs of 1902, and still one of the most popular in community song literature, regardless of the season.

Words by Ren Shields

Music by George Evans

With a lilt

1. There's a time in each year that we al-ways hold dear, Good old sum-mer - time, With the birds and the trees and sweet-scent-ed

2. To swim in the pool you'd play "hook-y" from school, Good old sum-mer - time, You'd play "ring a - ros - ie" with Jim, Kate and

Where Did You Get that Hat?

SULLIVAN, comedian and acrobatic dancer, home for vacation and searching in the attic for possible make-up material, came across an old plug hat, too small for his head and absurdly tall for his short, plump figure. Wearing it, he ventured into the street and was ridiculed and jeered at by a group of small boys, who yelled: "Where did you get that hat?" The phrase gave him the title for his celebrated song, one of the best-remembered hits of 1888, which for years after was sung and played everywhere.

Words and Music by Joseph J. Sullivan

1. Now how I came to get this hat 'tis ver-y strange and fun-ny: Grand-fa-ther died and left to me his prop-er-ty and mon-ey. And when the will it was read out, they told me straight and flat, If
2. If I go to the op-'ra house in the op-'ra sea-son, There's some-one sure to shout at me, with-out the slight-est rea-son. If I go to a "chow-der club," to have a jol-ly spree; There's
3. At twen-ty-one I thought I would to my sweet-heart be mar-ried, The peo-ple in the neigh-bor-hood had said too long we'd tar-ried. So off to church we went right quick, de-ter-mined to get wed; I

I Don't Want to Play in Your Yard

A NICELY told story of a quarrel between two little maids and of their reconciliation the following day. A well-known song of 1894.

Words by Philip Wingate

Music by H. W. Petrie

1. Once there lived, side by side, two lit-tle maids, Used to dress just a-like, hair down in braids;___ Blue ging-ham pin-a-fores, stock-ings of red, Lit-tle sun-bon-nets tied on each pret-ty head. When school was o-ver se-crets they'd

2. Next day two lit-tle maids each oth-er miss, Quar-rels are soon made up, sealed with a kiss.___ Then hand in hand a-gain, hap-py they go, Friends all thro' life to be, they love each oth-er so.___ Soon school days pass a-way, sor-rows and

Dmin.　　　　A7　　　　　　　Dmin. C7　F　　　C7

tell,　　Whis-per-ing arm in arm, down by the well.___ One day a quar-rel came,
bliss,　　But love re-mem-bers yet, quar-rels and kiss.___ In sweet dreams of child-hood,

Gmin. 7　　　A　　　D7　　　G7　　　C7　　　　F

hot tears were shed:　"You can't play in our yard," But the oth-er said:___
we hear the cry:　"You can't play in our yard," And the old re-ply:___

123

The Man Who Broke the Bank at Monte Carlo

IN 1891 there appeared on the streets of London a strange figure dressed in foppish attire, recklessly throwing money around, who called himself "The Man Who Broke the Bank at Monte Carlo." His name, so the story goes, was Arthur DeCourcey Bower, and his job was to be a sort of sandwich man advertising that most famous of gambling resorts, Monte Carlo.

Fred Gilbert, an English song writer, saw the words of the title used as a headline on a Strand Billboard in London. Caught by their rhythm, he set them to music. His song, at first rejected in England, was brought to America by William Hoey, who sang it with such success that he was never allowed to sing a concert without it. "It made of Hoey," says Douglas Gilbert, "a one song man; it became his trademark."

Words and Music by Fred Gilbert

With a bounce

1. I've just got here, thro' Pa-ris, from the sun-ny south-ern shore. I to
2. I stay in-doors till aft-er lunch, and then my dai-ly walk To the
3. I pa-tron-ized the ta-bles at the Mon-te Car-lo hell Till they

Mon-te Car-lo went, just to raise my win-ter's rent. Dame For-tune smiled up-
great Tri-um-phal Arch is one grand tri-um-phal march. Ob-served by each ob-
had-n't got a sou for a Christ-ian or a Jew. So___ I quick-ly went

on me as she'd nev-er done be-fore, And I've now such lots of mon-ey, I'm a
serv-er with the keen-ness of a hawk, I'm a mass of mon-ey, lin-en, silk, and
to Par-is for the charms of mad'-moiselle, Who's the load-stone of my heart what can I

CHORUS

1st time **p** , 2nd time **f**

As I walk a-long the Bois Boo-long With an in-de-pen-dent air,____ You can hear the girls de-

clare____ "He must be a mil-lion-aire." You can hear them sigh, And wish to die, You can

see them wink the oth-er eye At the man who broke the Bank at Mon-te Car - lo.____

ARE YOU THE O'REILLY?

(IS THAT YOU, MR. RILEY?)

ROONEY'S comic hit of 1883, "Is That You, Mr. Riley?" touched off a cycle of comic songs, all more or less imitations of his classic. The "Mr. Riley" of 1883 is better known today as "The O'Reilly," whom "they speak of so highly."

Words and Music by Pat Rooney

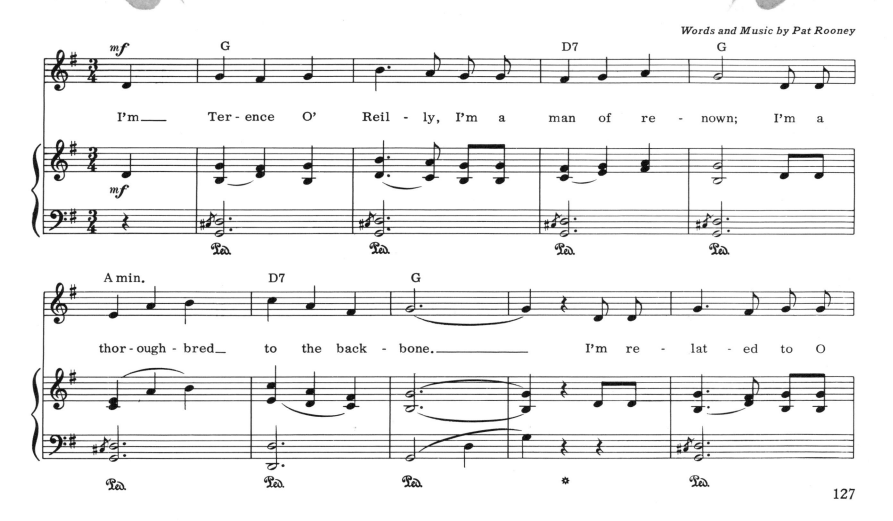

I'm___ Ter-ence O'Reil-ly, I'm a man of re-nown; I'm a thor-ough-bred___ to the back-bone.___ I'm re-lat-ed to O

Con - nor, my moth - er was Queen of Chi - na, ten miles from Ath -

lone._____ But if they'd let me be, I'd have Ire - land free; On the

rail - roads you would pay no fare._____ I'd have the U - nit - ed States

un - der my thumb, And I'd sleep in the Pres - i - dent's chair._____

COME HOME, FATHER

HENRY C. WORK, a well-known writer of war songs, was an ardent abolitionist and also wrote many songs to help the cause of temperance. The most famous of these is "Come Home, Father," the story of a child seeking her father at a saloon to take him home to the bedside of his little son, who is dying.

Words and Music by Henry Clay Work

poor broth-er Ben - ny so sick in her arms, And no one to help her but me. Come
this is the mes-sage she sent me to bring: "Come quick-ly, or he will be gone." Come
these were the ver - y last words that he said: "I want to kiss Pa - pa good night." Come

home! come home! come home! Please, fa - ther, dear fa - ther, come home.
home! come home! come home! Please, fa - ther, dear fa - ther, come home.
home! come home! come home! Please, fa - ther, dear fa - ther, come home.

CHORUS

Hear the sweet voice of the child Which the night winds re-peat as they roam! Oh,

who could re-sist this most plain-tive of prayers? "Please, fa -ther, dear fa - ther, come home!"

132

Please Go 'Way and Let Me Sleep

THIS SONG is generally credited to Harry Von Tilzer, but he seems only to have published it. It was composed by James T. Brymn, a Negro musician who led the 350th Field Artillery band during the first World War. The band later toured the country as the "Black Devils." The song, immensely popular in 1902, was used for years afterward in vaudeville and in the early movies.

Words by R. C. McTherson

Music by James T. Brymn

1. I am twice as hap-py as a mil - lion - aire,— Ev - 'ry day I have such love - ly dreams. When I'm sleep - in' mon - ey nev - er gives me a care,— Trou-ble nev - er trou-bles me it seems. I don't mind no sum - mer heat or

2. Ten o' - clock this morn-in' I was pound-in' my ear,— Dream-in' I'm the warm-est man in town. Land-lord hol-lered "Wake up quick an' get out of here,— Hur - ry up, the place is burn - ing down!" I got sore at be - in' woke an'

never had a dream so nice, Thought I was in Par - a - dise.

Wak - in' up makes me feel cheap, So please let me sleep.

135

MAPLE LEAF RAG

SCOTT JOPLIN, a Negro pianist, was born in Texarkana, Texas, in 1868. At the age of seventeen, he went to St. Louis and for eight years played piano-rag in the honky-tonks there. He then went to Sedalia and there wrote his first compositions, sentimental songs. But he continued to play piano-rag, notably at a place called The Maple Leaf Club.

There he was heard by a "rag" enthusiast, John Stillwell Stark, and, influenced by him, published in 1899 his first ragtime composition, "Original Rag." This was followed the same year by "Maple Leaf Rag." These, with Kerry Mills' "Georgia Camp Meeting" (1897), were the first published rags. Joplin wrote, in all, thirty-nine piano-rags. His name is one of the greatest associated with the development of ragtime.

Words by Sydney Brown

Music by Scott Joplin

Allegro moderato

1. I came from ole Vir-gin-ny, from the coun-ty Ac-o-mac, I___ have no wealth to speak of 'cept the clothes up-on my back. I can do the coun-try hoe-down, I can buck and wing to show down, And

2. I dropped in-to the swell-est ball, the great ex-clu-sive it, But my face was dead a-gainst me, and my trou-sers did-n't fit. But when Ma-ple Leaf was start-ed my ti-mid-i-ty de-part-ed, I

3. The men were struck with jeal-ous-y, the ra-zors 'gan to flash, But the la-dies gath-er'd round me, for I'd sure-ly made a mash. The___ fin-est belle, she sent a boy to call a coach and four. We

DANCE

COMRADES

"COMRADES," written in 1887 and of English origin, was widely popular in America by 1894.

Words and Music by Felix McGlennon

Tempo di Marcia

1. We from child-hood played to-geth-er, My dear com-rade Jack and
2. When just bud-ding in-to man-hood I yearn'd for a sol-dier's
3. I en-list-ed, Jack came with me, And ups and downs we

I. We would fight each oth-er's bat-tles, To each oth-er's aid we'd
life. Night and day I dream'd of glo-ry, Long-ing for the bat-tle's
shared. For a time our lives were peace-ful, But at length war was de-

fly. And in boy-ish scrapes and trou-bles You would find us
strife. I said, "Jack, I'll be a sol-dier, 'Neath the Red, the
clared. Eng-land's flag had been in-sult-ed; We were or-dered

ev-'ry-where. Where one went the oth-er fol-lowed,Nought could part us an-y-where.
White and Blue. Good-bye, Jack."Said he: "No, nev-er, If you go, then I'll go, too."
to the front. And the Reg'-ment we be-longed to Had to bear the bat-tle's brunt.

CHORUS
Tempo di Valse

We were com - rades, com - rades, ev-er since we were

boys, _____ Shar-ing each oth - er's sor - rows,

shar-ing each oth - er's joys. _____ Com-rades when man-hood was

threat-ened my dar-ling old com-rade was there by my side. _____ *Fine*

4th verse agitato

4. In the night the sav-age foe-men, Crept a-round us as we lay, To our arms we leap'd and

faced them, Back to back we stood at bay. As I fought, a sav-age at me Aimed his

spear like light-ning's dart; But my com-rade sprang to save me And re-ceiv'd it in his heart. _____

143

Aloha Oe

LILIUOKALANI was the last reigning queen of the Hawaiian Islands. She ascended the throne in 1891, was dethroned in 1893 because of her attempt to brush aside political reforms. Two years later she unsuccessfully attempted to regain the throne and then formally renounced her royal claims. She wrote many songs, "Aloha Oe," for which she is generally given credit, being the best known. The melody of the verse is from a much earlier song by Charles C. Converse entitled "The Rock Beside the Sea."

Words and Music by Liliuokalani, Queen of the Hawaiian Islands

Proud-ly swept the rain-cloud by the cliff, As on it glid-ed by the trees; Still __ fol - low-ing with grief the "liko," The A - hi-hi le-hu - a of the vale. _____ Fare-well to thee, ____ fare-well to

THE YANKEE DOODLE BOY

FROM the musical show,

Little Johnny Jones.   See page 33.

Words and Music by George M. Cohan

THE STARS AND STRIPES FOREVER

THIS FAMOUS military march, Sousa's unquestioned masterpiece, was written under strange circumstances. Sousa and his wife were returning from a vacation in Italy which had been cut short by the sudden death of Sousa's manager, David Blakely. According to a story attributed to Sousa, on the ocean voyage he heard in his mind, day after day, strains of band music and unfamiliar melodies. Upon his arrival in New York he wrote down the music as he had heard it—"The Stars and Stripes Forever."

Words and Music by John Philip Sousa

1. Let mar-tial note In tri-umph float, And lib-er-ty ex-tend its might-y hand. A flag ap-pears, 'Mid

2. Let ea-gle shriek From loft-y peak, The nev-er-end-ing watch-word of our land. Let sum-mer breeze Waft

150

thun - d'rous cheers, The ban-ner of the West-ern land. The em - blem of the
through the trees; The ech - o of the cho-rus grand. Sing out for lib - er-

brave and true, Its folds pro-tect no ty - rant crew, The red and white and star-ry blue, Is
ty and light, Sing out for free-dom and the right. Sing out for Un - ion and its might, Oh,

Free-dom's shield and hope. Oth - er na - tions may deem their flags the best, And ___
pa - tri - ot - ic Sons!

cheer them with fer - vid e - la - tion. But the flag of the North and

South and West Is the flag of flags, The flag of Free - dom's na - tion.

CHORUS

Hur - rah for the flag of the free; _____ May it wave as our stand - ard for -

ev - er. The gem of the land and the sea, _____ The

Index of Titles

Index of First Lines

Index of First Lines of Choruses

Index of Authors and Composers